MW00615514

TREE QUOTES

MariJo Moore

TREE QUOTES

FIFTH PRINTING 2016

COPYRIGHT © 1998 MARIJO MOORE

ART COPYRIGHT © 1998 DARRIN BARK
(EXCEPT LEAVES GATHERED BY MARIJO
MOORE)

ALL RIGHTS RESERVED.

NO PORTION OF THIS BOOK MAY BE
REPRODUCED IN ANY FORM WITHOUT
WRITTEN PERMISSION FROM THE
PUBLISHER.

RENEGADE PLANETS PUBLISHING
ASHEVILLE, NC
MARIJOMOORE.COM

ISBN #0-9654921-4-1

LAYOUT & DESIGN
FIREFLYINX.COM

For the

Trees and the long shadows they cast.

May those who do not respect you
begin to realize the horrible loss caused by
clear cutting, acid rain, and neglect.

And for those who do care,
may the forest always be
with you.

This morning a grove of hemlocks said,
"We are more concerned for your
future than ours."

Trees are sometimes quiet, like the moon.
And sometimes, they breathe sounds
that can be heard for generations.

Life will use your wants and insecurities
to teach you your most valuable lessons.

Little willows welcome big tears.

You must never question from

where the gift comes.

There is only one source

and you are a part of this source.

Many times a heart opens only

enough to let in tiny bits of light.

Open your heart wide to heal.

Humans cannot understand the depth of

their own wisdom.

This would be too great a shock.

Life is a mixture of

sweet rain and rotten leaves.

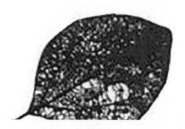

Some days you get the bear.
Some days the bear gets you.
And some days,
you can't even find the woods.

The sun spreads across the sky
and silver leaves smile warmly,
knowing that all is as it should be
at any given moment.

We trees live in the place
of the origin of dreams,
where rain sings to itself,
and memories coexist harmoniously.
Visit with us often.

There is nothing more beautiful than harmony.

Light brings destruction to what has lived

inside the darkness for too, too long.

Trees are necessary, as is clean water.

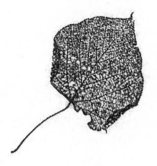

The mysteries belong to our Mother.

Imaginary winds can only lick at
what will never be,
whereas those truly felt but not ignored
offer invitations to enjoy otherworldly gifts.

Seek your answers inside your own heart.
Time has come to stop searching for the opinions of
others on matters of your spiritual growth.

Enter the deepest part of a situation with
your eyes wide open, then look to see
where you have been.

Listen to our barks.

*Clear out your dreams by asking
for clarification from those
who float in occasionally.*

Dreams are filters of manifestations.

Trees just grow.

Look into the heart of things.

Sometimes, in the melting of a moment,

an idea forms itself from the residue

and those who pay attention

are those to whom the blessings

reveal themselves.

Manage your time quietly and sufficiently,

and always allow time for play.

Carry the sweetest part of a memory in your eyes,

the best part in your heart,

and the worst part in your hands

so you can throw it away

at a moment's notice.

You know it is time for a change whenever

anger at yourself wells inside

causing your heart to hurt.

Listen to the pines whispering,
"Quietly our roots grow deep into the mysterious.
You never stop complaining
long enough to grow."

Look behind the rainbow.
There's another, and another,
and another...

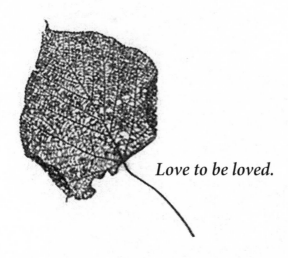

Love to be loved.

This afternoon, a fallen oak log spoke
into the quietness of the forest,
"Don't worry so much about achievement.
Concentrate on sharing with others
what you have been given."

Follow your intentions through and see what happens along the way toward completion.

Hiding secrets will never be as important as revealing truths through creative efforts.

Remember this.

You are at your weakest moment
when you pretend to be at your strongest.

Deep love blossoms
after survival of tepid thunderstorms.
These are necessary
but not healthy on a daily basis.
Seek the balance.

To question your motives is the most

timely gift you can give yourself.

Search beneath the roots of discontent

for the disturbing realities of truth.

If Spirit is the source of creation,
why can't creativity lead you back to
the source?

So many times humans pretend to know
what they desire so as not to appear lost.
Occasionally becoming lost is
essential to following one's true path.

Crows are our buddies.

Whatever is essential to survive today
may not be as necessary tomorrow.
Do not fret, await the dawning,
then rethink the importance.

Shatter old dreams by picking up new ones.

To those who expect everything,
nothing is ever enough.
Have fewer expectations and
more periods of gratefulness.

Tiny drops of perspiration cause one
to glow with spiritual success.

The soul speaks in silence.
The silence left behind
haunting music, hard rains,
children's laughter, and long-remembered
autumn days.

Greedy people can never experience the
real beauty of trees for their desires
are not strong or deep.
They can never reach the miracles
generous souls and trees witness daily.

Whoever told you you cannot see
one answer inside another?
Look again.

Do you doubt your importance?

Don't.

You've struggled far too long

over empty nests.

When one is empty, take apart and begin anew.

The greatest secret of life

is knowing when to let go.

Too many times you look under

shade trees for rest and comfort,

when the true healings remain

in the full sun.

The ground moves with birds feeding.

Seek the reasons for being alive
in your smallest accomplishments.

This evening, as the sun and moon
began to exchange places,
a majestic maple sang
through its leaves,
"Share your deepest fears
with an old, mighty tree.
Don't forget to walk
beside the rivers,
and remember to gently
and constantly
encourage the little ones."

You knew these things all along.
You just had to be reminded.

MariJo Moore (Cherokee/Irish Descent) is an author/ editor/anthologist/psychic/medium. The author of over twenty books including A Book of Ceremonies and Spiritual Energies Thereof, When the Dead Dream, Red Woman With Backward Eyes and Other Stories, The Boy With a Tree Growing from His Ear and Other Stories, Crow Quotes, and Bear Quotes. She is also editor of several anthologies including Unraveling the Spreading Cloth of Time Indigenous Thoughts Concerning the Universe. She resides in the mountains of western NC.

MariJoMoore.com

Artist Darrin Bark is of Cherokee descent and resides in Cherokee, North Carolina. The cover drawing features his maternal great-grandmother Minda Reed of the Wolf Clan.

Thank you for supporting an independently owned business.

RENEGADE PLANETS PUBLISHING

81112329R00024

Made in the USA
Columbia, SC
16 November 2017